DEDICATION

This goal planner is dedicated to YOU, a young leader who is going to change the world.

This goal planner belongs to:

_____

Leadership4Kids

Publisher: Leadership4Kids
Cover Design: Peter J. Liang

Library of Congress Cataloging-in-Publication Data

Liang, Peter J.

I AM A LEADER: A 90-DAY GOAL PLANNER FOR KIDS/Peter J. Liang

p. cm.

ISBN: 978-1-952477-07-2

1. Self-Help   2. Leadership Development   3. Education   4. Self-Awareness

0 1 2 3 4 5 6 7 8 9
Printed in the United States of America

Leadership4Kids Goal Planner
Parent's Getting Started Guide

START WITH WHY - Spend a few minutes to reflect why you got this goal planner and what do you hope your child will gain from a daily journaling and goal planning practice.

GET EXCITED - Share with your child that you are excited about this planner. Explain to your child why inspirations/topics such as gratitude, self-awareness, goal setting and growth mindset, are important in life and this journal helps her/him learn these skills through self-discovery.

DAY 1 – READY, SET, GO! - Read the step by step "how to" next and do the "top 3 goals", "why", "main actions" and "brainstorm" together with your child. As this is a new experience for your child, give appropriate time for discussion related to the writing prompts.

FIRST 7 DAYS – If possible, do the planner together for the first 7 days, to answer any questions your child might have. Set up a routine. Many parents incorporate it into their homework routine, as a way to reflect and plan for the next day.

CELEBRATE - At the end of Week 1, discuss with your child what she/he has learned. Brainstorm together how to put these ideas into action. More importantly, do something to celebrate. Whether your child spent 10 minutes or 10 seconds doing this, just keep encouraging them to continue on this journey of self-discovery.

What is the "I AM A LEADER" Goal Planner?

Welcome to the "I AM A LEADER" Goal Planner. Through this planner, you are embarking on a 90-day journey to develop leadership qualities and attitudes that will help you grow and live a fulfilled and exciting life.

The planner is broken down into the following sections:

- Guided Goal Setting
    - Your Top 3 Goals
    - Why?
    - Main Actions
- 90-Day Daily Planner
    - Week 1 – Week 4
    - Checkpoint 1
    - Week 5 – Week 8
    - Checkpoint 2
    - Week 9 – Week 12
- Summary
    - Goals Achieved
    - Lessons Learned
    - What goals would you like to achieve next?

Ready to begin your **I AM A LEADER** Goal Planner adventure? **Let's start with Goal Setting!**

Top 3 Goals

What are your main goals for the next 90 days?

1. _____

_____

_____

2. _____

_____

_____

3. _____

_____

_____

Goal Setting - write down your top 3 goals that you want to achieve in the next 90 days. Big or small, your goals should be S.M.A.R.T:

- **S**pecific
- **M**easurable
- **A**chievable
- **R**elevant
- **T**ime-based

Example of some S.M.A.R.T. goals

- Do well on the up and coming Math final and get at least a 90
- Organize a toy drive for our church before Christmas
- Get the MVP award for basketball at the end of the season

Why these goals?

Why are these goals important to you?

1. _____
   _____
   _____

2. _____
   _____
   _____

3. _____
   _____
   _____

This is the most important part of goals setting. Your motivation for each goal has to be strong and clear. If your why is not meaningful to you, it will be very hard to focus.

Example of Whys
- I like math and I want to prove to myself that I can do well.
- I know other kids aren't as fortunate. So I want them to have some toys for Christmas.
- Last season I didn't play so well, I want to show my teammates I can do much better.

Actions

What will you do to achieve your goals?

	Actions	When
1.		
2.		
3.		

For each one of your 3 goals, jot down 3 actions that you will take to help you get closer to your goals every day.

Example of Actions

- Take 1 practice quiz a day, before the final exam.
- Tell all my friends about the toy drive, by end of this week.
- Practice on my own 3 times/week and focus on dribbling, for the next 3 months

If you are not sure what to do here, it's perfectly OK. Try a little brainstorming (see next page) and/or ask your parent/teacher for help.

Brainstorm

Use this space here for brainstorming to help you come up with ideas, or anything else that comes to mind when you think about your goals. Remember, when you brainstorm, all ideas are good ideas. Have fun!

How to fill out the daily entries

1. **Start with this "centering" exercise.**

   - **3 Deep Breaths** – Allow your tongue to hang loose and your belly get soft. Breath in slowly through your nose and out through your mouth. When you inhale, make sure your tummy gets bigger.

   - **Smiling Heart** – Everyone has something or someone that makes them happy inside -- perhaps a friend, a toy, a flower, a song. Sit with your eyes closed and spend a moment picturing whatever it is that makes you smile inside.

   - **Shine** – Imagine that you are the sun or a lightbulb. What do you do? You shine. Feel every inch of your skin glowing outward as you shine in every direction possible.

2. **Follow the prompts on each page**

   - Morning happiness meter
   - Read Today's inspiration quote
   - Today, I am grateful for
   - Top 5 actions towards my goals
   - I AM affirmation
   - Daily reflection/lessons learned
   - My energy level
   - Tomorrow, I will...

   See the next pages for examples.

3. **This is YOUR goal planner. Enjoy and have fun!**

Example 1

My morning

☹ ☹ 😐 🙂 😄

Centering

☑ 3 Deep Breaths   ☑ Smiling Heart   ☑ Shine

Today's inspiration

Whether you think you can or think you can't – you are right.

Henry Ford

Today, I am grateful for...

1 My mom for getting lots of food for my family.

2 The people working to make things for me.

3 The things I get to do if I want.

Review your goals

Today's top 5 actions towards your goals.

☑ practice quizlet 1 time today

☑ have a practice quiz today

☑ get 1 hour of studying done

☑ do 30min of review

☑ Make flashcards for math

I AM Affirmation

I AM

A mathematian

Daily Reflection/Lessons Learned/Notes

I can do anything if I belive in myself.

My energy level

(battery icons)

Tomorrow, I will...

1 Have a fun day

2 I will be productive

3 be kind and understanding

Example 2

My morning

☹ ☹ 😐 😊 😄

Centering

☑ 3 Deep Breaths   ☑ Smiling Heart   ☑ Shine

Today's inspiration

Believe you can and
you are halfway
there.

Theodore Roosevelt

Today, I am grateful for...

1 My teachers for teaching
me so many things

2 Myself for working hard

3 Freedom because I can
do whatever I want

Review your goals

**Today's top 5
actions towards
your goals.**

☑ I practiced 3x3.
☑ Learned new thing in math.
☑ I brainstormed some new ideas.
☑ Did research for cubing comps.
☑ I got 100 on my practice year
test.

I AM Affirmation

I AM

a good cuber

Daily Reflection/Lessons Learned/Notes

I learned that I am
more powerful than I
think.

My energy level

Tomorrow, I will...

1 Do more research for cubing

2 Pratice more 3x3.

3 See my cousins

A Few Tips...

- Pick a time each day that works for you. Perhaps when you get home from school or right after dinner. The key is to be consistent.

- It's okay if you are not sure what to do. Ask your parent for help.

- If you need some help with the centering exercise, you can find a guided audio version here https://leadership4kids.com/blogs/learn/centering

- This goal planner is all about YOU. There is no right or wrong way of doing it. At any point, if you prefer not to follow the prompt, it's perfectly okay. Simply follow your heart, use the space, and write down whatever you feel.

Ready, Set, Let's Go!

You have just learned how to use the "I AM A LEADER" Goal Planner. We are excited for you to begin your 90-day adventure. Turn the page and complete Day 1. now.

WEEK 1

A journey of a thousand miles begins
with a single step.

— Confucius

Day 1

Today's Date: _____ / _____ / 20 _____

My morning

☹ ☹ 😐 🙂 😀

Centering

☐ 3 Deep Breaths　　☐ Smiling Heart　　☐ Shine

Today's inspiration

We must be the change we want to see in the world.

Mahatma Gandhi

Today, I am grateful for...

1 _____

_____

2 _____

_____

3 _____

_____

Review your goals

Today's top 5 actions towards your goals.

☐ _____

☐ _____

☐ _____

☐ _____

☐ _____

I AM Affirmation

I AM

_____

Daily Reflection/Lessons Learned/Notes

_____

_____

_____

My energy level

🔋 🔋 🔋 🔋 🔋

Tomorrow, I will...

1 _____

2 _____

3 _____

Day 2

Today's Date: _____/_____/ 20_____

My morning

☹ ☹ 😐 🙂 😀

Centering

☐ 3 Deep Breaths ☐ Smiling Heart ☐ Shine

Whether you think you can or think you can't – you are right.

Henry Ford

Today, I am grateful for...

1 _____

2 _____

3 _____

Review your goals

Today's top 5 actions towards your goals.

☐ _____

☐ _____

☐ _____

☐ _____

☐ _____

I AM Affirmation

I AM

_____

Daily Reflection/Lessons Learned/Notes

My energy level

🔋🔋🔋🔋🔋

Tomorrow, I will...

1 _____

2 _____

3 _____

Day 3

Today's Date: _____/_____/ 20_____

My morning

☹ ☹ 😐 🙂 😊

Centering

☐ 3 Deep Breaths   ☐ Smiling Heart   ☐ Shine

Today's inspiration

If you see it in your mind, you will hold it in your hand.

Bob Proctor

Today, I am grateful for...

1 _____

_____

2 _____

_____

3 _____

_____

Review your goals

Today's top 5 actions towards your goals.

☐ _____

☐ _____

☐ _____

☐ _____

☐ _____

I AM Affirmation

I AM

_____

Daily Reflection/Lessons Learned/Notes

_____

_____

_____

My energy level

🔋 🔋 🔋 🔋 🔋

Tomorrow, I will...

1 _____

2 _____

3 _____

Day 4

Today's Date: _____/_____/ 20_____

My morning

☹ ☹ 😐 🙂 😊

Centering

☐ 3 Deep Breaths   ☐ Smiling Heart   ☐ Shine

Today's inspiration

Passion is energy.
Feel the power that
comes from focusing
on what excites you.

Oprah Winfrey

Today, I am grateful for...

1

2

3

Review your goals

Today's top 5
actions towards
your goals.

☐

☐

☐

☐

☐

I AM Affirmation

I AM

_____

Daily Reflection/Lessons Learned/Notes

My energy level

Tomorrow, I will...

1

2

3

Day 5

Today's Date: _____/_____/ 20_____

My morning
😣 😟 😐 🙂 😄

Centering
☐ 3 Deep Breaths   ☐ Smiling Heart   ☐ Shine

Today's inspiration

Fall seven times,
stand up eight.

Japanese Proverb

Today, I am grateful for...

1
_____

_____

2
_____

_____

3
_____

_____

Review your goals

Today's top 5
actions towards
your goals.

☐ _____

☐ _____

☐ _____

☐ _____

☐ _____

I AM Affirmation

I AM

_____

Daily Reflection/Lessons Learned/Notes

_____

_____

_____

My energy level

Tomorrow, I will...

1
_____

2
_____

3
_____

Day 6

My morning

☹ 😟 😐 🙂 😀

Centering

☐ 3 Deep Breaths   ☐ Smiling Heart   ☐ Shine

Today's inspiration

The greater danger for most of us isn't that our aim is too high and miss it, but that it is too low and we reach it.

Michelangelo

Today, I am grateful for...

1
_____

2
_____

3
_____

Review your goals

Today's top 5 actions towards your goals.

☐ _____

☐ _____

☐ _____

☐ _____

☐ _____

I AM Affirmation

I AM

_____

Daily Reflection/Lessons Learned/Notes

_____
_____
_____

My energy level

Tomorrow, I will...

1
_____

2
_____

3
_____

Day 7

My morning

😧 😟 😐 🙂 😄

Centering

☐ 3 Deep Breaths   ☐ Smiling Heart   ☐ Shine

Today's inspiration

Every action in our lives touches on some chord that will vibrate in eternity.

Edwin Hubbel Chapin

Today, I am grateful for...

1 _____

2 _____

3 _____

Review your goals

Today's top 5 actions towards your goals.

☐ _____

☐ _____

☐ _____

☐ _____

☐ _____

I AM Affirmation

I AM

_____

Daily Reflection/Lessons Learned/Notes

_____

_____

_____

My energy level

Tomorrow, I will...

1 _____

2 _____

3 _____

WEEK 2

After all, all knowledge simply means
self knowledge.

- Bruce Lee

Day 8

Today's Date: _____ / _____ / 20_____

My morning

😖 😕 😐 🙂 😄

Centering

☐ 3 Deep Breaths ☐ Smiling Heart ☐ Shine

Today's inspiration

Every great story on the planet happened when someone decided not to give up, but kept going no matter what.

Spryte Loriano

Today, I am grateful for...

1 _____

2 _____

3 _____

Review your goals

Today's top 5 actions towards your goals.

☐ _____

☐ _____

☐ _____

☐ _____

☐ _____

I AM Affirmation

I AM

_____

Daily Reflection/Lessons Learned/Notes

_____

_____

_____

My energy level

🔋 🔋 🔋 🔋 🔋

Tomorrow, I will...

1 _____

2 _____

3 _____

Day 9

Today's Date: _____/_____/ 20_____

My morning

😟 😔 😐 🙂 😀

Centering

☐ 3 Deep Breaths   ☐ Smiling Heart   ☐ Shine

Today's inspiration

Why fit in when you were born to stand out?

Dr. Suess

Today, I am grateful for...

1 _____

2 _____

3 _____

Review your goals

Today's top 5 actions towards your goals.

☐ _____

☐ _____

☐ _____

☐ _____

☐ _____

I AM Affirmation

I AM

_____

Daily Reflection/Lessons Learned/Notes

My energy level

Tomorrow, I will...

1 _____

2 _____

3 _____

Day 10

My morning

😣 😦 😐 🙂 😃

Centering

☐ 3 Deep Breaths   ☐ Smiling Heart   ☐ Shine

Today's inspiration

Yesterday is history. Tomorrow is a mystery. Today is a gift. That's why we call it 'The Present'.

Eleanor Roosevelt

Today, I am grateful for...

1
_____

2
_____

3
_____

Review your goals

Today's top 5 actions towards your goals.

☐
☐
☐
☐
☐

I AM Affirmation

I AM

_____

Daily Reflection/Lessons Learned/Notes

My energy level

🔋🔋🔋🔋🔋

Tomorrow, I will...

1
_____

2
_____

3

Day 11

Today's Date: _____/_____/ 20_____

My morning

☹ ☹ 😐 🙂 😀

Centering

☐ 3 Deep Breaths   ☐ Smiling Heart   ☐ Shine

Today's inspiration

Strength and growth come only through continuous effort.

Napoleon Hill

Today, I am grateful for...

1 _____

2 _____

3 _____

Review your goals

Today's top 5 actions towards your goals.

☐ _____
☐ _____
☐ _____
☐ _____
☐ _____

I AM Affirmation

I AM

_____

Daily Reflection/Lessons Learned/Notes

_____

My energy level

Tomorrow, I will...

1 _____

2 _____

3 _____

Day 12

Today's Date: _____ / _____ / 20_____

My morning

😣 😟 😐 🙂 😊

Centering

☐ 3 Deep Breaths   ☐ Smiling Heart   ☐ Shine

Today's inspiration

Strength does not come from winning. When you go through hardships and decide not to surrender, that is strength.

Arnold Schwarzenegger

Today, I am grateful for...

1

2

3

Review your goals

Today's top 5 actions towards your goals.

☐
☐
☐
☐
☐

I AM Affirmation

I AM

_____

Daily Reflection/Lessons Learned/Notes

My energy level

Tomorrow, I will...

1

2

3

Day 13

Today's Date: _____/_____/ 20_____

My morning

😫 😟 😐 🙂 😄

Centering

☑ 3 Deep Breaths   ☐ Smiling Heart   ☐ Shine

Today's inspiration

Without goals, and plans to reach them, you are like a ship that has set sail with no destination.

Fitzhugh Dodson

Today, I am grateful for...

1 _____

2 _____

3 _____

Review your goals

Today's top 5 actions towards your goals.

☐ _____

☐ _____

☐ _____

☐ _____

☐ _____

I AM Affirmation

I AM

_____

Daily Reflection/Lessons Learned/Notes

_____

_____

_____

My energy level

🔋🔋🔋🔋🔋

Tomorrow, I will...

1 _____

2 _____

3 _____

Day 14

Today's Date: _____ / _____ / 20_____

My morning

😧 😟 😐 🙂 😊

Centering

☐ 3 Deep Breaths   ☐ Smiling Heart   ☐ Shine

Today's inspiration

You always pass failure on the way to success.

Mickey Rooney

Today, I am grateful for...

1 _____

2 _____

3 _____

Review your goals

Today's top 5 actions towards your goals.

☐ _____
☐ _____
☐ _____
☐ _____
☐ _____

I AM Affirmation

I AM

_____

Daily Reflection/Lessons Learned/Notes

_____
_____
_____

My energy level

Tomorrow, I will...

1 _____

2 _____

3 _____

WEEK 3

I learned that courage was not the
absence of fear, but the triumph over
it. The brave man is not he who does
not feel afraid, but he who conquers
that fear.

– Nelson Mandela

Day 15

My morning

😣 😦 😐 🙂 😄

Centering

☐ 3 Deep Breaths   ☐ Smiling Heart   ☐ Shine

Today's inspiration

You have to be able to get up and dust yourself off and always be going forward.

Rita Moreno

Today, I am grateful for...

1 _____

2 _____

3 _____

Review your goals

Today's top 5 actions towards your goals.

☐ _____

☐ _____

☐ _____

☐ _____

☐ _____

I AM Affirmation

I AM

_____

Daily Reflection/Lessons Learned/Notes

_____

_____

_____

My energy level

[battery icons]

Tomorrow, I will...

1 _____

2 _____

3 _____

Day 16

My morning

☹ ☹ 😐 🙂 😀

Centering

☐ 3 Deep Breaths   ☐ Smiling Heart   ☐ Shine

Today's inspiration

To win big, you sometimes have to take big risks.

Bill Gates

Today, I am grateful for...

1 _____

2 _____

3 _____

Review your goals

Today's top 5 actions towards your goals.

☐ _____
☐ _____
☐ _____
☐ _____
☐ _____

I AM Affirmation

I AM

_____

Daily Reflection/Lessons Learned/Notes

My energy level

🔋 🔋 🔋 🔋 🔋

Tomorrow, I will...

1 _____

2 _____

3 _____

Day 17

Today's Date: _____/_____/ 20_____

My morning
😠 😦 😐 🙂 😄

Centering
☐ 3 Deep Breaths   ☐ Smiling Heart   ☐ Shine

Today's inspiration

Make each day your masterpiece.

John Wooden

Today, I am grateful for...

1 _____

_____

2 _____

_____

3 _____

_____

Review your goals

Today's top 5 actions towards your goals.

☐ _____

☐ _____

☐ _____

☐ _____

☐ _____

I AM Affirmation

I AM

_____

Daily Reflection/Lessons Learned/Notes

_____

_____

_____

My energy level

🔋🔋🔋🔋🔋

Tomorrow, I will...

1 _____

2 _____

3 _____

Day 18

My morning

☹ ☹ 😐 🙂 😊

Centering

☐ 3 Deep Breaths ☐ Smiling Heart ☐ Shine

Today's inspiration

It always seems impossible until it's done.

Nelson Mandela

Today, I am grateful for...

1

2

3

Review your goals

Today's top 5 actions towards your goals.

☐

☐

☐

☐

☐

I AM Affirmation

I AM

_____

Daily Reflection/Lessons Learned/Notes

My energy level

🔋🔋🔋🔋🔋

Tomorrow, I will...

1

2

3

Day 19

My morning

☹ ☹ 😐 🙂 😀

Centering

☐ 3 Deep Breaths   ☐ Smiling Heart   ☐ Shine

Today's inspiration

If you set your goals ridiculously high and it's a failure, you will fail above everyone else's success.

James Cameron

Today, I am grateful for...

1

2

3

Review your goals

Today's top 5 actions towards your goals.

☐
☐
☐
☐
☐

I AM Affirmation

I AM

_____

Daily Reflection/Lessons Learned/Notes

My energy level

Tomorrow, I will...

1

2

3

Day 20

Today's Date: _____/_____/ 20_____

My morning

☹ ☹ 😐 🙂 😊

Centering

☐ 3 Deep Breaths   ☐ Smiling Heart   ☐ Shine

Today's inspiration

Everyone's dream can come true if you just stick to it and work hard.

Serena Williams

Today, I am grateful for...

1 _____

2 _____

3 _____

Review your goals

Today's top 5 actions towards your goals.

☐ _____

☐ _____

☐ _____

☐ _____

☐ _____

I AM Affirmation

I AM

_____

Daily Reflection/Lessons Learned/Notes

_____

_____

_____

My energy level

🔋🔋🔋🔋🔋

Tomorrow, I will...

1 _____

2 _____

3 _____

Day 21

Today's Date: _____ / _____ / 20_____

My morning

☹ ☹ 😐 🙂 😀

Centering

☐ 3 Deep Breaths   ☐ Smiling Heart   ☐ Shine

Today's inspiration

If you want to live a happy life, tie it to a goal, not to people or things.

Albert Einstein

Today, I am grateful for...

1 _____

2 _____

3 _____

Review your goals

Today's top 5 actions towards your goals.

☐ _____

☐ _____

☐ _____

☐ _____

☐ _____

I AM Affirmation

I AM

_____

Daily Reflection/Lessons Learned/Notes

_____

_____

_____

My energy level

Tomorrow, I will...

1 _____

2 _____

3 _____

WEEK 4

Change the way you look at things and the things you look at change.

– Dr. Wayne W. Dyer

Day 22

Today's Date: _____ / _____ / 20____

My morning

☹ ☹ 😐 🙂 😀

Centering

☐ 3 Deep Breaths   ☐ Smiling Heart   ☐ Shine

Today's inspiration

Just start. Nothing
is insurmountable.

Lin-Manuel Miranda

Today, I am grateful for...

1 _____

2 _____

3 _____

Review your goals

Today's top 5
actions towards
your goals.

☐
☐
☐
☐
☐

I AM Affirmation

I AM

_____

Daily Reflection/Lessons Learned/Notes

My energy level

🔋 🔋 🔋 🔋 🔋

Tomorrow, I will...

1 _____

2 _____

3 _____

Day 23

My morning

☹ ☹ 😐 🙂 😀

Centering

☐ 3 Deep Breaths ☐ Smiling Heart ☐ Shine

Today's inspiration

Envision, create, and believe in your own universe, and the universe will form around you.

Tony Hsieh

Today, I am grateful for...

1 _____

2 _____

3 _____

Review your goals

Today's top 5 actions towards your goals.

☐ _____

☐ _____

☐ _____

☐ _____

☐ _____

I AM Affirmation

I AM

_____

Daily Reflection/Lessons Learned/Notes

_____

_____

_____

My energy level

🔋🔋🔋🔋🔋

Tomorrow, I will...

1 _____

2 _____

3 _____

Day 24

Today's Date: _____ / _____ / 20 _____

My morning

☹ 😦 😐 🙂 😀

Centering

☐ 3 Deep Breaths   ☐ Smiling Heart   ☐ Shine

Today's inspiration

Change starts when you write it down and make it real.

Christie Love

Today, I am grateful for...

1 _____

_____

2 _____

_____

3 _____

_____

Review your goals

Today's top 5 actions towards your goals.

☐ _____

☐ _____

☐ _____

☐ _____

☐ _____

I AM Affirmation

I AM

_____

Daily Reflection/Lessons Learned/Notes

_____

_____

_____

My energy level

🔋 🔋 🔋 🔋 🔋

Tomorrow, I will...

1 _____

2 _____

3 _____

Day 25

My morning

☹ 🙁 😐 🙂 😃

Centering

☐ 3 Deep Breaths   ☐ Smiling Heart   ☐ Shine

Today's inspiration

I fear failure, but I won't let it stop me. Sometimes you just got to do it or else it just doesn't happen.

Mark Cuban

Today, I am grateful for...

1

2

3

Review your goals

Today's top 5 actions towards your goals.

☐
☐
☐
☐
☐

I AM Affirmation

I AM

_____

Daily Reflection/Lessons Learned/Notes

My energy level

Tomorrow, I will...

1

2

3

Day 26

My morning

☹ ☹ 😐 🙂 😊

Centering

☐ 3 Deep Breaths   ☐ Smiling Heart   ☐ Shine

Today's inspiration

No one is perfect –
that's why pencils
have erasers.

Wolfgang Riebe

Today, I am grateful for...

1 _____

_____

2 _____

_____

3 _____

_____

Review your goals

Today's top 5
actions towards
your goals.

☐ _____

☐ _____

☐ _____

☐ _____

☐ _____

I AM Affirmation

I AM

_____

Daily Reflection/Lessons Learned/Notes

_____

_____

_____

_____

My energy level

🔋 🔋 🔋 🔋 🔋

Tomorrow, I will...

1 _____

2 _____

3 _____

Day 27

My morning

☹ ☹ 😐 🙂 😀

Centering

☐ 3 Deep Breaths   ☐ Smiling Heart   ☐ Shine

Today's inspiration

Don't just read the easy stuff. You may be entertained by it, but you will never grow from it.

John Rohn

Today, I am grateful for...

1 _____

2 _____

3 _____

Review your goals

Today's top 5 actions towards your goals.

☐ _____
☐ _____
☐ _____
☐ _____
☐ _____

I AM Affirmation

I AM

_____

Daily Reflection/Lessons Learned/Notes

_____

My energy level

Tomorrow, I will...

1 _____

2 _____

3 _____

Day 28

Today's Date: _____ / _____ / 20_____

My morning

😣 😟 😐 🙂 😊

Centering

☐ 3 Deep Breaths   ☐ Smiling Heart   ☐ Shine

Today's inspiration

Only surround yourself with people who will lift you higher.

Oprah Winfrey

Today, I am grateful for...

1 _____

_____

2 _____

_____

3 _____

_____

Review your goals

Today's top 5 actions towards your goals.

☐ _____

☐ _____

☐ _____

☐ _____

☐ _____

I AM Affirmation

I AM

_____

Daily Reflection/Lessons Learned/Notes

_____

_____

_____

My energy level

🔋 🔋 🔋 🔋 🔋

Tomorrow, I will...

1 _____

2 _____

3 _____

Checkpoint: Your Goals

How are you doing with your goals? Have you completed any of your goals? If so, make sure you celebrate your achievements, big or small. What about any new goals in mind? Perfect, just add these new goals to the list below for the next 8 weeks.

1.

2.

3.

4.

5.

Checkpoint: Your Actions

What will you do next to achieve your goals?

Actions	By When?
1.	
2.	
3.	
4.	
5.	

WEEK 5

Failure is so important. We speak about
success all the time. It is the ability to
learn from failure that often leads to
greater success.

– J.K. Rowling

Day 29

Today's Date: _____ / _____ / 20_____

My morning

☹ ☹ 😐 🙂 😄

Centering

☐ 3 Deep Breaths   ☐ Smiling Heart   ☐ Shine

Today's inspiration

This one step –
choosing a goal and
sticking to it –
changes everything.

Scott Reed

Today, I am grateful for...

1 ....

....

2 ....

....

3 ....

....

Review your goals

Today's top 5
actions towards
your goals.

☐ ....

☐ ....

☐ ....

☐ ....

☐ ....

I AM Affirmation

I AM

_____

Daily Reflection/Lessons Learned/Notes

....

....

....

My energy level

🔋🔋🔋🔋🔋

Tomorrow, I will...

1 ....

2 ....

3 ....

Day 30

Today's Date: _____/_____/ 20_____

My morning

☹ ☹ 😐 🙂 😊

Centering

☐ 3 Deep Breaths ☐ Smiling Heart ☐ Shine

Today's inspiration

What you get by achieving your goals is not as important as what you become by achieving your goals.

Zig Ziglar

Today, I am grateful for...

1 _____

2 _____

3 _____

Review your goals

Today's top 5 actions towards your goals.

☐ _____
☐ _____
☐ _____
☐ _____
☐ _____

I AM Affirmation

I AM

_____

Daily Reflection/Lessons Learned/Notes

_____

My energy level

Tomorrow, I will...

1 _____

2 _____

3 _____

Day **31**

My morning

☹ ☹ 😐 🙂 😀

Centering

☐ 3 Deep Breaths   ☐ Smiling Heart   ☐ Shine

Today's inspiration

Discipline is the bridge between goals and accomplishment.

Jim Rohn

Today, I am grateful for...

1

2

3

Review your goals

Today's top 5 actions towards your goals.

☐

☐

☐

☐

☐

I AM Affirmation

I AM

_____

Daily Reflection/Lessons Learned/Notes

My energy level

Tomorrow, I will...

1

2

3

Day 32

My morning

☹ ☹ 😐 🙂 😊

Centering

☐ 3 Deep Breaths   ☐ Smiling Heart   ☐ Shine

Today's inspiration

Change your thinking, change your life.

Ernest Holmes

Today, I am grateful for...

1 _____

2 _____

3 _____

Review your goals

Today's top 5 actions towards your goals.

☐ _____

☐ _____

☐ _____

☐ _____

☐ _____

I AM Affirmation

I AM

_____

Daily Reflection/Lessons Learned/Notes

_____

_____

_____

My energy level

🔋 🔋 🔋 🔋 🔋

Tomorrow, I will...

1 _____

2 _____

3 _____

Day 33

My morning

☹ ☹ 😐 🙂 😃

Centering

☐ 3 Deep Breaths ☐ Smiling Heart ☐ Shine

Today's inspiration

Always be a first-rate version of yourself, instead of a second-rate version of somebody else.

Judy Garland

Today, I am grateful for...

1 _____

2 _____

3 _____

Review your goals

Today's top 5 actions towards your goals.

☐ _____
☐ _____
☐ _____
☐ _____
☐ _____

I AM Affirmation

I AM

_____

Daily Reflection/Lessons Learned/Notes

_____

My energy level

🔋🔋🔋🔋🔋

Tomorrow, I will...

1 _____

2 _____

3 _____

Day 34

My morning

😫 😟 😐 🙂 😄

Centering

☐ 3 Deep Breaths   ☐ Smiling Heart   ☐ Shine

Today's inspiration

Life begins at the end of your comfort zone.

Neale Donald Walsh

Today, I am grateful for...

1

2

3

Review your goals

Today's top 5 actions towards your goals.

☐
☐
☐
☐
☐

I AM Affirmation

I AM

_____

Daily Reflection/Lessons Learned/Notes

My energy level

Tomorrow, I will...

1

2

3

Day **35**

My morning

😫 😟 😐 🙂 😃

Centering

☐ 3 Deep Breaths   ☐ Smiling Heart   ☐ Shine

Today's inspiration

The people who are crazy enough to think they can change the world are the ones who do.

Steve Jobs

Today, I am grateful for...

1

2

3

Review your goals

Today's top 5 actions towards your goals.

☐
☐
☐
☐
☐

I AM Affirmation

I AM

_____

Daily Reflection/Lessons Learned/Notes

My energy level

Tomorrow, I will...

1

2

3

WEEK 6

The challenge of leadership is to be strong, but not rude; be kind, but not weak; be bold, but not bully; be humble, but not timid; be proud, but not arrogant.

– Jim Rohn

Day 36

My morning

☹ ☹ ☺ ☺ ☺

Centering

☐ 3 Deep Breaths   ☐ Smiling Heart   ☐ Shine

Today's inspiration

What the mind can conceive and believe, it can achieve.

Napoleon Hill

Today, I am grateful for...

1 _____

_____

2 _____

_____

3 _____

_____

Review your goals

Today's top 5 actions towards your goals.

☐ _____

☐ _____

☐ _____

☐ _____

☐ _____

I AM Affirmation

I AM

_____

Daily Reflection/Lessons Learned/Notes

_____

_____

_____

My energy level

🔋🔋🔋🔋🔋

Tomorrow, I will...

1 _____

2 _____

3 _____

Day 37

My morning

☹ ☹ 😐 🙂 😃

Centering

☐ 3 Deep Breaths   ☐ Smiling Heart   ☐ Shine

Today's inspiration

Be yourself;
everyone else is
already taken.

Oscar Wilde

Today, I am grateful for...

1

2

3

Review your goals

Today's top 5
actions towards
your goals.

☐
☐
☐
☐
☐

I AM Affirmation

I AM

_____

Daily Reflection/Lessons Learned/Notes

My energy level

Tomorrow, I will...

1

2

3

Day 38

My morning

☹ 😦 😐 🙂 😀

Centering

☐ 3 Deep Breaths   ☐ Smiling Heart   ☐ Shine

Today's inspiration

I will not let anyone walk through my mind with their dirty feet.

Mahatma Gandhi

Today, I am grateful for...

1

2

3

Review your goals

Today's top 5 actions towards your goals.

☐
☐
☐
☐
☐

I AM Affirmation

I AM

_____

Daily Reflection/Lessons Learned/Notes

My energy level

🔋 🔋 🔋 🔋 🔋

Tomorrow, I will...

1

2

3

Day 39

My morning

☹ ☹ 😐 🙂 😊

Centering

☐ 3 Deep Breaths   ☐ Smiling Heart   ☐ Shine

Today's inspiration

The meaning of life is to find your gift. The PURPOSE of life is to give it away.

Pablo Picass

Today, I am grateful for...

1 _____

2 _____

3 _____

Review your goals

Today's top 5 actions towards your goals.

☐ _____

☐ _____

☐ _____

☐ _____

☐ _____

I AM Affirmation

I AM

_____

Daily Reflection/Lessons Learned/Notes

_____

_____

_____

My energy level

[battery icons]

Tomorrow, I will...

1 _____

2 _____

3 _____

Day 40

My morning

☹ ☹ 😐 🙂 😀

Centering

☐ 3 Deep Breaths   ☐ Smiling Heart   ☐ Shine

Today's inspiration

How many cares one loses when one decides not to be something but to be someone.

Coco Chanel

Today, I am grateful for...

1 _____

2 _____

3 _____

Review your goals

Today's top 5 actions towards your goals.

☐ _____
☐ _____
☐ _____
☐ _____
☐ _____

I AM Affirmation

I AM

_____

Daily Reflection/Lessons Learned/Notes

_____

My energy level

🔋🔋🔋🔋🔋

Tomorrow, I will...

1 _____

2 _____

3 _____

Day 41

Today's Date: _____ / _____ / 20_____

My morning

😟 😦 😐 🙂 😊

Centering

☐ 3 Deep Breaths ☐ Smiling Heart ☐ Shine

Today's inspiration

I think goals should never be easy, they should force you to work, even if they are uncomfortable at the time.

Michael Phelps

Today, I am grateful for...

1 _____

2 _____

3 _____

Review your goals

Today's top 5 actions towards your goals.

☐ _____
☐ _____
☐ _____
☐ _____
☐ _____

I AM Affirmation

I AM

_____

Daily Reflection/Lessons Learned/Notes

_____
_____
_____

My energy level

🔋🔋🔋🔋🔋

Tomorrow, I will...

1 _____

2 _____

3 _____

Day 42

My morning

☹ 🙁 😐 🙂 😀

Centering

☐ 3 Deep Breaths   ☐ Smiling Heart   ☐ Shine

Today's inspiration

If you feel stuck, stop, reset, refocus and keep going.

Unknown

Today, I am grateful for...

1

2

3

Review your goals

Today's top 5 actions towards your goals.

☐
☐
☐
☐
☐

I AM Affirmation

I AM

_____

Daily Reflection/Lessons Learned/Notes

My energy level

🔋🔋🔋🔋🔋

Tomorrow, I will...

1

2

3

WEEK 7

If you want to lift yourself up, lift up someone else."

– Booker T. Washington

Day 43

My morning

☹ ☹ 😐 🙂 😊

Centering

☐ 3 Deep Breaths   ☐ Smiling Heart   ☐ Shine

Today's inspiration

In the middle of every difficulty lies opportunity.

Albert Einstein

Today, I am grateful for...

1

2

3

Review your goals

Today's top 5 actions towards your goals.

☐
☐
☐
☐
☐

I AM Affirmation

I AM

_____

Daily Reflection/Lessons Learned/Notes

My energy level

Tomorrow, I will...

1

2

3

Day 44

Today's Date: _____/_____/ 20_____

My morning

☹ ☹ 😐 🙂 😀

Centering

☐ 3 Deep Breaths   ☐ Smiling Heart   ☐ Shine

Today's inspiration

Dreams are not what you see in your sleep, dreams are things which do not let you sleep.

Cristiano Ronaldo

Today, I am grateful for...

1

2

3

Review your goals

Today's top 5 actions towards your goals.

☐
☐
☐
☐
☐

I AM Affirmation

I AM

_____

Daily Reflection/Lessons Learned/Notes

My energy level

Tomorrow, I will...

1

2

3

Day 45

My morning

☹ ☹ 😐 🙂 😊

Centering

☐ 3 Deep Breaths   ☐ Smiling Heart   ☐ Shine

Today's inspiration

Never let the odds keep you from doing what you know in your heart you were meant to do.

H. Jackson Brown, Jr.

Today, I am grateful for...

1 _____

2 _____

3 _____

Review your goals

Today's top 5 actions towards your goals.

☐ _____
☐ _____
☐ _____
☐ _____
☐ _____

I AM Affirmation

I AM

_____

Daily Reflection/Lessons Learned/Notes

_____
_____
_____

My energy level

🔋🔋🔋🔋🔋

Tomorrow, I will...

1 _____

2 _____

3 _____

Day 46

Today's Date: _____/_____/ 20_____

☹ ☹ 😐 🙂 😃

Centering
☐ 3 Deep Breaths   ☐ Smiling Heart   ☐ Shine

Today's inspiration

Either I will find a way,
or I will make one.

Philip Sidney

Today, I am grateful for...

1 _____

2 _____

3 _____

Review your goals

Today's top 5
actions towards
your goals.

☐ _____
☐ _____
☐ _____
☐ _____
☐ _____

I AM Affirmation

I AM

_____

Daily Reflection/Lessons Learned/Notes

_____
_____
_____

My energy level

🔋 🔋 🔋 🔋 🔋

Tomorrow, I will...

1 _____

2 _____

3 _____

Day 47

My morning

☹ 😦 😐 🙂 😀

Centering

☐ 3 Deep Breaths   ☐ Smiling Heart   ☐ Shine

Today's inspiration

Arriving at one goal is the starting point to another.

John Dewey

Today, I am grateful for...

1 _____

2 _____

3 _____

Review your goals

Today's top 5 actions towards your goals.

☐ _____

☐ _____

☐ _____

☐ _____

☐ _____

I AM Affirmation

I AM

_____

Daily Reflection/Lessons Learned/Notes

_____

_____

_____

My energy level

Tomorrow, I will...

1 _____

2 _____

3 _____

Day 48

Today's Date: _____/_____/ 20_____

My morning

😣 😟 😐 🙂 😄

Centering

☐ 3 Deep Breaths   ☐ Smiling Heart   ☐ Shine

Today's inspiration

Success is the progressive realization of a worthy goal or ideal.

Earl Nightingale

Today, I am grateful for...

1

2

3

Review your goals

Today's top 5 actions towards your goals.

☐
☐
☐
☐
☐

I AM Affirmation

I AM

_____

Daily Reflection/Lessons Learned/Notes

My energy level

Tomorrow, I will...

1

2

3

Day 49

My morning

☹ ☹ 😐 🙂 😊

Centering

☐ 3 Deep Breaths   ☐ Smiling Heart   ☐ Shine

Today's inspiration

If you spend too much time thinking about a thing, you'll never get it done.

Bruce Lee

Today, I am grateful for...

1 _____

2 _____

3 _____

Review your goals

Today's top 5 actions towards your goals.

☐ _____

☐ _____

☐ _____

☐ _____

☐ _____

I AM Affirmation

I AM

_____

Daily Reflection/Lessons Learned/Notes

_____

_____

_____

My energy level

🔋🔋🔋🔋🔋

Tomorrow, I will...

1 _____

2 _____

3 _____

WEEK 8

If you can see your path laid out in front of you step by step, you know it's not your path. Your own path you have to make with every step you take. That's why it's YOUR path.

– Joseph Campbell

Day 50

Today's Date: _____ / _____ / 20_____

My morning

☹ ☹ 😐 🙂 😊

Centering

☐ 3 Deep Breaths ☐ Smiling Heart ☐ Shine

Today's inspiration

Always keep a positive mindset, it will improve your outlook on the world.

Roald Dahl

Today, I am grateful for...

1 _____

2 _____

3 _____

Review your goals

Today's top 5 actions towards your goals.

☐ _____

☐ _____

☐ _____

☐ _____

☐ _____

I AM Affirmation

I AM

_____

Daily Reflection/Lessons Learned/Notes

_____

_____

_____

My energy level

🔋 🔋 🔋 🔋 🔋

Tomorrow, I will...

1 _____

2 _____

3 _____

Day 51

Today's Date: _____ / _____ / 20_____

My morning
☹ ☹ 😐 🙂 😃

Centering
☐ 3 Deep Breaths   ☐ Smiling Heart   ☐ Shine

Today's inspiration

The memories you have tomorrow are created by the actions you take today.

Jean Lauzier

Today, I am grateful for...

1

2

3

Review your goals

Today's top 5 actions towards your goals.

☐
☐
☐
☐
☐

I AM Affirmation

I AM

_____

Daily Reflection/Lessons Learned/Notes

My energy level

Tomorrow, I will...

1

2

3

Day 52

Today's Date: _____/_____/ 20_____

My morning

☹ 😦 😐 🙂 😊

Centering

☐ 3 Deep Breaths   ☐ Smiling Heart   ☐ Shine

Today's inspiration

Imagination is more important than knowledge.

Albert Einstein

Today, I am grateful for...

1 _____

2 _____

3 _____

Review your goals

Today's top 5 actions towards your goals.

☐ _____
☐ _____
☐ _____
☐ _____
☐ _____

I AM Affirmation

I AM

_____

Daily Reflection/Lessons Learned/Notes

_____
_____
_____
_____

My energy level

🔋🔋🔋🔋🔋

Tomorrow, I will...

1 _____

2 _____

3 _____

Day 53

My morning

☹ ☹ 😐 🙂 😀

Centering

☐ 3 Deep Breaths   ☐ Smiling Heart   ☐ Shine

Today's inspiration

If you spend too much time thinking about a thing, you'll never get it done.

Bruce Lee

Today, I am grateful for...

1 _____

2 _____

3 _____

Review your goals

Today's top 5 actions towards your goals.

☐ _____
☐ _____
☐ _____
☐ _____
☐ _____

I AM Affirmation

I AM

_____

Daily Reflection/Lessons Learned/Notes

_____

_____

_____

My energy level

🔋🔋🔋🔋🔋

Tomorrow, I will...

1 _____

2 _____

3 _____

Day 54

Today's Date: _____ / _____ / 20 _____

My morning

☹ ☹ 😐 🙂 😊

Centering

☑ 3 Deep Breaths ☐ Smiling Heart ☐ Shine

Today's inspiration

Be kind whenever possible. It is always possible.

Dalai Lama

Today, I am grateful for...

1 _____

2 _____

3 _____

Review your goals

Today's top 5 actions towards your goals.

- ☐ _____
- ☐ _____
- ☐ _____
- ☐ _____
- ☐ _____

I AM Affirmation

I AM

_____

Daily Reflection/Lessons Learned/Notes

_____

_____

_____

My energy level

🔋 🔋 🔋 🔋 🔋

Tomorrow, I will...

1 _____

2 _____

3 _____

Day 55

My morning

☹ ☹ 😐 🙂 😊

Centering

☐ 3 Deep Breaths ☐ Smiling Heart ☐ Shine

Today's inspiration

Mix a little foolishness with your serious plans. It is lovely to be silly at the right moment.

Horace

Today, I am grateful for...

1 _____

2 _____

3 _____

Review your goals

Today's top 5 actions towards your goals.

☐ _____
☐ _____
☐ _____
☐ _____
☐ _____

I AM Affirmation

I AM

_____

Daily Reflection/Lessons Learned/Notes

_____
_____
_____

My energy level

Tomorrow, I will...

1 _____

2 _____

3 _____

Day 56

Today's Date: _____ / _____ / 20 _____

My morning

☹ ☹ 😐 🙂 😊

Centering

☐ 3 Deep Breaths   ☐ Smiling Heart   ☐ Shine

Today's inspiration

The only person who never makes a mistake is someone who never does anything.

Theodore Roosevelt

Today, I am grateful for...

1 _____

_____

2 _____

_____

3 _____

_____

Review your goals

Today's top 5 actions towards your goals.

☐ _____
☐ _____
☐ _____
☐ _____
☐ _____

I AM Affirmation

I AM

_____

Daily Reflection/Lessons Learned/Notes

_____

_____

_____

My energy level

🔋🔋🔋🔋🔋

Tomorrow, I will...

1 _____

2 _____

3 _____

Checkpoint: Your Goals

How are you doing with your goals? Have you completed any of your goals? If so, make sure you celebrate your achievements, big or small. What about any new goals in mind? Perfect, just add these new goals to the list below for the next 4 weeks.

1.

2.

3.

4.

5.

Checkpoint: Your Actions

What will you do next to achieve your goals?

	Actions	By When?
1.		
2.		
3.		
4.		
5.		

WEEK 9

Some people want it to happen, some wish it would happen, others make it happen.

— Michael Jordan

Day 57

Today's Date: _____/_____/ 20_____

My morning

😣 😟 😐 🙂 😊

Centering

☐ 3 Deep Breaths   ☐ Smiling Heart   ☐ Shine

Today's inspiration

There are better starters than me but I'm a strong finisher.

Usain Bolt

Today, I am grateful for...

1
2
3

Review your goals

Today's top 5 actions towards your goals.

☐
☐
☐
☐
☐

I AM Affirmation

I AM

_____

Daily Reflection/Lessons Learned/Notes

My energy level

🔋🔋🔋🔋🔋

Tomorrow, I will...

1
2
3

Day 58

My morning

☹ 🙁 😐 🙂 😀

Centering

☐ 3 Deep Breaths   ☐ Smiling Heart   ☐ Shine

Today's inspiration

The time is always right to do what is right.

Martin Luther King, Jr.

Today, I am grateful for...

1

2

3

Review your goals

Today's top 5 actions towards your goals.

☐
☐
☐
☐
☐

I AM Affirmation

I AM

_____

Daily Reflection/Lessons Learned/Notes

My energy level

Tomorrow, I will...

1

2

3

Day **59**

Today's Date: _____ / _____ / 20_____

My morning

😖 😣 😐 🙂 😄

Centering

☐ 3 Deep Breaths   ☐ Smiling Heart   ☐ Shine

Today's inspiration

Many of life's failures are people who did not realize how close they were to success when they gave up.

Thomas Edison

Today, I am grateful for...

1 _____

2 _____

3 _____

Review your goals

Today's top 5 actions towards your goals.

☐ _____
☐ _____
☐ _____
☐ _____
☐ _____

I AM Affirmation

I AM

_____

Daily Reflection/Lessons Learned/Notes

_____
_____
_____

My energy level

🔋 🔋 🔋 🔋 🔋

Tomorrow, I will...

1 _____

2 _____

3 _____

Day 60

My morning

☹ 😕 😐 🙂 😊

Centering

☐ 3 Deep Breaths   ☐ Smiling Heart   ☐ Shine

Today's inspiration

In any moment of decision, the best thing you can do is the right thing. The worst thing you can do is nothing.

Theodore Roosevelt

Today, I am grateful for...

1 _____

2 _____

3 _____

Review your goals

Today's top 5 actions towards your goals.

☐
☐
☐
☐
☐

I AM Affirmation

I AM

_____

Daily Reflection/Lessons Learned/Notes

My energy level

Tomorrow, I will...

1 _____

2 _____

3 _____

Day 61

My morning

😣 😕 😐 🙂 😄

Centering

☐ 3 Deep Breaths   ☐ Smiling Heart   ☐ Shine

Today's inspiration

Strong convictions precede great actions.

Louisa May Alcott

Today, I am grateful for...

1

2

3

Review your goals

Today's top 5 actions towards your goals.

☐
☐
☐
☐
☐

I AM Affirmation

I AM

_____

Daily Reflection/Lessons Learned/Notes

My energy level

🔋 🔋 🔋 🔋 🔋

Tomorrow, I will...

1

2

3

Day 62

Today's Date: _____/_____/ 20_____

My morning

☹ ☹ 😐 🙂 😄

Centering

☐ 3 Deep Breaths   ☐ Smiling Heart   ☐ Shine

Today's inspiration

Reach high, for stars lie hidden in your soul. Dream deep, for every dream precedes the goal.

Pamela Vaull Starr

Today, I am grateful for...

1 _____

2 _____

3 _____

Review your goals

Today's top 5 actions towards your goals.

☐ _____
☐ _____
☐ _____
☐ _____
☐ _____

I AM Affirmation

I AM

_____

Daily Reflection/Lessons Learned/Notes

_____
_____
_____
_____

My energy level

🔋🔋🔋🔋🔋

Tomorrow, I will...

1 _____

2 _____

3 _____

Day **63**

Today's Date: _____/_____/ 20_____

My morning

☹ ☹ 😐 🙂 😃

Centering

☐ 3 Deep Breaths   ☐ Smiling Heart   ☐ Shine

Today's inspiration

The secret of getting ahead is getting started.

Mark Twain

Today, I am grateful for...

1 _____

2 _____

3 _____

Review your goals

Today's top 5 actions towards your goals.

☐ _____

☐ _____

☐ _____

☐ _____

☐ _____

I AM Affirmation

I AM

_____

Daily Reflection/Lessons Learned/Notes

_____

_____

_____

My energy level

Tomorrow, I will...

1 _____

2 _____

3 _____

WEEK 10

You may encounter many defeats, but you must not be defeated. In fact, it may be necessary to encounter the defeats, so you can know who you are, what you can rise from, how you can still come out of it.

– Maya Angelou

Day 64

My morning

😣 😦 😐 🙂 😄

Centering

☐ 3 Deep Breaths   ☐ Smiling Heart   ☐ Shine

Today's inspiration

Hold yourself responsible for a higher standard than anybody expects of you. Never excuse yourself.

Henry Ward Beecher

Today, I am grateful for...

1

2

3

Review your goals

Today's top 5 actions towards your goals.

☐
☐
☐
☐
☐

I AM Affirmation

I AM

_____

Daily Reflection/Lessons Learned/Notes

My energy level

🔋🔋🔋🔋🔋

Tomorrow, I will...

1

2

3

Day 65

Today's Date: _____ / _____ / 20 _____

My morning

😧 😟 😐 🙂 😄

Centering

☐ 3 Deep Breaths   ☐ Smiling Heart   ☐ Shine

Today's inspiration

Never give up on what you really want to do. The person with big dreams is more powerful than one with all the facts.

Albert Einstein

Today, I am grateful for...

1 _____

2 _____

3 _____

Review your goals

Today's top 5 actions towards your goals.

☐ _____

☐ _____

☐ _____

☐ _____

☐ _____

I AM Affirmation

I AM

_____

Daily Reflection/Lessons Learned/Notes

_____

_____

_____

My energy level

Tomorrow, I will...

1 _____

2 _____

3 _____

Day 66

Today's Date: _____ / _____ / 20 _____

My morning

☹ ☹ 😐 🙂 😀

Centering

☐ 3 Deep Breaths   ☐ Smiling Heart   ☐ Shine

Today's inspiration

Being different isn't a bad thing. It means you're brave enough to be yourself.

Luna Lovegood

Today, I am grateful for...

1

2

3

Review your goals

Today's top 5 actions towards your goals.

☐

☐

☐

☐

☐

I AM Affirmation

I AM

_____

Daily Reflection/Lessons Learned/Notes

My energy level

Tomorrow, I will...

1

2

3

Day 67

Today's Date: _____/_____/ 20_____

My morning
😣 😟 😐 🙂 😄

Centering
☐ 3 Deep Breaths   ☐ Smiling Heart   ☐ Shine

Today's inspiration

I have not failed.
I've just found
10,000 ways that
won't work.

Thomas Edison

Today, I am grateful for...

1 _____

2 _____

3 _____

Review your goals

Today's top 5
actions towards
your goals.

☐ _____
☐ _____
☐ _____
☐ _____
☐ _____

I AM Affirmation

I AM

_____

Daily Reflection/Lessons Learned/Notes

_____

_____

_____

My energy level

🔋🔋🔋🔋🔋

Tomorrow, I will...

1 _____

2 _____

3 _____

Day 68

Today's Date: _____ / _____ / 20_____

My morning

☹ ☹ 😐 🙂 😊

Centering

☐ 3 Deep Breaths   ☐ Smiling Heart   ☐ Shine

Today's inspiration

You're braver than you believe and stronger than you seem, and smarter than you think.

A.A. Milne

Today, I am grateful for...

1

2

3

Review your goals

Today's top 5 actions towards your goals.

☐
☐
☐
☐
☐

I AM Affirmation

I AM

_____

Daily Reflection/Lessons Learned/Notes

My energy level

Tomorrow, I will...

1

2

3

Day 69

My morning

☹ ☹ 😐 🙂 😊

Centering

☐ 3 Deep Breaths   ☐ Smiling Heart   ☐ Shine

Today's inspiration

We are what we repeatedly do. Excellence, therefore, is not an act but a habit.

Aristotle

Today, I am grateful for...

1 _____

2 _____

3 _____

Review your goals

Today's top 5 actions towards your goals.

☐ _____
☐ _____
☐ _____
☐ _____
☐ _____

I AM Affirmation

I AM

_____

Daily Reflection/Lessons Learned/Notes

_____
_____
_____

My energy level

🔋🔋🔋🔋🔋

Tomorrow, I will...

1 _____

2 _____

3 _____

Day 70

Today's Date: _____/_____/ 20_____

My morning

☹ ☹ 😐 🙂 😄

Centering

☐ 3 Deep Breaths ☐ Smiling Heart ☐ Shine

Today's inspiration

Give the world the best you have, and the best will come to you.

Madeline Bridge

Today, I am grateful for...

1

2

3

Review your goals

Today's top 5 actions towards your goals.

☐
☐
☐
☐
☐

I AM Affirmation

I AM

_____

Daily Reflection/Lessons Learned/Notes

My energy level

Tomorrow, I will...

1

2

3

WEEK 11

I have learned over the years that when one's mind is made up, this diminishes fear; knowing what must be done does away with fear.

- Rosa Parks

Day 71

Today's Date: _____/_____/ 20_____

My morning

☹ 😦 😐 🙂 😊

Centering

☐ 3 Deep Breaths ☐ Smiling Heart ☐ Shine

Today's inspiration

You are not meant for crawling. You have wings. Learn to use them.

Rumi

Today, I am grateful for...

1 _____

2 _____

3 _____

Review your goals

Today's top 5 actions towards your goals.

☐ _____

☐ _____

☐ _____

☐ _____

☐ _____

I AM Affirmation

I AM

_____

Daily Reflection/Lessons Learned/Notes

_____

_____

_____

My energy level

Tomorrow, I will...

1 _____

2 _____

3 _____

Day 72

Today's Date: _____ / _____ / 20 _____

My morning

☹ ☹ 😐 🙂 😀

Centering

☐ 3 Deep Breaths   ☐ Smiling Heart   ☐ Shine

Today's inspiration

We must all face the choice between what is right and what is easy.

Albus Dumbledore

Today, I am grateful for...

1 ....

2 ....

3 ....

Review your goals

Today's top 5 actions towards your goals.

☐ ....

☐ ....

☐ ....

☐ ....

☐

I AM Affirmation

I AM

_____

Daily Reflection/Lessons Learned/Notes

....

....

....

My energy level

🔋🔋🔋🔋🔋

Tomorrow, I will...

1 ....

2 ....

3 ....

Day 73

Today's Date: _____ / _____ / 20_____

My morning

☹ ☹ 😐 🙂 😊

Centering

☐ 3 Deep Breaths   ☐ Smiling Heart   ☐ Shine

Today's inspiration

If you can dream it,
you can do it.

Walt Disney

Today, I am grateful for...

1 _____

2 _____

3 _____

Review your goals

Today's top 5
actions towards
your goals.

☐ _____

☐ _____

☐ _____

☐ _____

☐ _____

I AM Affirmation

I AM

_____

Daily Reflection/Lessons Learned/Notes

_____

_____

_____

My energy level

🔋🔋🔋🔋🔋

Tomorrow, I will...

1 _____

2 _____

3 _____

Day 74

My morning

☹ 😦 😐 🙂 😀

Centering

☐ 3 Deep Breaths   ☐ Smiling Heart   ☐ Shine

Today's inspiration

Wonder is the beginning of wisdom.

Socrates

Today, I am grateful for...

1 _____

2 _____

3 _____

Review your goals

Today's top 5 actions towards your goals.

☐ _____

☐ _____

☐ _____

☐ _____

☐ _____

I AM Affirmation

I AM

_____

Daily Reflection/Lessons Learned/Notes

_____

_____

_____

My energy level

🔋🔋🔋🔋🔋

Tomorrow, I will...

1 _____

2 _____

3 _____

Day 75

Today's Date: _____/_____/ 20_____

My morning

☹ ☹ 😐 🙂 😊

Centering

☐ 3 Deep Breaths   ☐ Smiling Heart   ☐ Shine

Today's inspiration

Two roads diverged in a wood, and I — I took the one less traveled by, And that has made all the difference.

Robert Frost

Today, I am grateful for...

1

2

3

Review your goals

Today's top 5 actions towards your goals.

☐
☐
☐
☐
☐

I AM Affirmation

I AM

_____

Daily Reflection/Lessons Learned/Notes

My energy level

🔋🔋🔋🔋🔋

Tomorrow, I will...

1

2

3

Day 76

Today's Date: _____ / _____ / 20 _____

My morning

☹ ☹ 😐 🙂 😊

Centering

☐ 3 Deep Breaths   ☐ Smiling Heart   ☐ Shine

Today's inspiration

The more that you read, the more things you will know. The more you learn, the more places you'll go!

Dr. Suess

Today, I am grateful for...

1 _____

2 _____

3 _____

Review your goals

Today's top 5 actions towards your goals.

☐ _____
☐ _____
☐ _____
☐ _____
☐ _____

I AM Affirmation

I AM

_____

Daily Reflection/Lessons Learned/Notes

_____
_____
_____

My energy level

🔋🔋🔋🔋🔋

Tomorrow, I will...

1 _____

2 _____

3 _____

Day 77

My morning

😧 😟 😐 🙂 😄

Centering

☐ 3 Deep Breaths   ☐ Smiling Heart   ☐ Shine

Today's inspiration

Never doubt yourself, it will only hold you back.

J.M. Barrie

Today, I am grateful for...

1

2

3

Review your goals

Today's top 5 actions towards your goals.

☐
☐
☐
☐
☐

I AM Affirmation

I AM

_____

Daily Reflection/Lessons Learned/Notes

My energy level

Tomorrow, I will...

1

2

3

WEEK 12

Stand Tall and Proud

Sink your roots deeply into the Earth

Reflect the light of a greater source

Think long term

Go out on a limb...

Be flexible

Remember your roots

Enjoy the view!

— Advice from a Tree

Day 78

Today's Date: _____ / _____ / 20 _____

My morning

☹ ☹ 😐 🙂 😀

Centering

☐ 3 Deep Breaths ☐ Smiling Heart ☐ Shine

Today's inspiration

Nothing is more honorable than a grateful heart.

Seneca

Today, I am grateful for...

1

2

3

Review your goals

Today's top 5 actions towards your goals.

☐
☐
☐
☐
☐

I AM Affirmation

I AM

_____

Daily Reflection/Lessons Learned/Notes

My energy level

Tomorrow, I will...

1

2

3

Day 79

Today's Date: _____ / _____ / 20_____

My morning
☹ ☹ 😐 🙂 😃

Centering
☐ 3 Deep Breaths   ☐ Smiling Heart   ☐ Shine

Today's inspiration

Rest in reason;
move in passion.

Khalil Gibran

Today, I am grateful for...

1

2

3

Review your goals

Today's top 5
actions towards
your goals.

☐
☐
☐
☐
☐

I AM Affirmation

I AM

_____

Daily Reflection/Lessons Learned/Notes

My energy level

Tomorrow, I will...

1

2

3

Day 80

Today's Date: _____ / _____ / 20_____

My morning

☹ ☹ 😐 🙂 😀

Centering

☐ 3 Deep Breaths   ☐ Smiling Heart   ☐ Shine

Today's inspiration

You're braver than you believe, stronger than you seem, and smarter than you think.

A.A. Milne

Today, I am grateful for...

1

2

3

Review your goals

Today's top 5 actions towards your goals.

☐
☐
☐
☐
☐

I AM Affirmation

I AM

_____

Daily Reflection/Lessons Learned/Notes

My energy level

🔋 🔋 🔋 🔋 🔋

Tomorrow, I will...

1

2

3

Day 81

Today's Date: _____/_____/ 20_____

My morning

😫 😟 😐 🙂 😀

Centering

☐ 3 Deep Breaths   ☐ Smiling Heart   ☐ Shine

Today's inspiration

Why fit in when you are born to stand out!

Dr. Suess

Today, I am grateful for...

1 _____

2 _____

3 _____

Review your goals

Today's top 5 actions towards your goals.

☐ _____

☐ _____

☐ _____

☐ _____

☐ _____

I AM Affirmation

I AM

_____

Daily Reflection/Lessons Learned/Notes

_____

_____

_____

My energy level

🔋🔋🔋🔋🔋

Tomorrow, I will...

1 _____

2 _____

3 _____

Day 82

My morning

☹ ☹ 😐 🙂 😄

Centering

☐ 3 Deep Breaths   ☐ Smiling Heart   ☐ Shine

Today's inspiration

Life is a gift.

Unknown

Today, I am grateful for...

1 _____

2 _____

3 _____

Review your goals

Today's top 5 actions towards your goals.

☐ _____
☐ _____
☐ _____
☐ _____
☐ _____

I AM Affirmation

I AM

_____

Daily Reflection/Lessons Learned/Notes

_____
_____
_____

My energy level

🔋🔋🔋🔋🔋

Tomorrow, I will...

1 _____

2 _____

3 _____

Day 83

Today's Date: _____/_____/ 20_____

My morning

😩 😟 😐 🙂 😄

Centering

☐ 3 Deep Breaths ☐ Smiling Heart ☐ Shine

Today's inspiration

We make a living by what we get, but we make a life by what we give.

Winston Churchill

Today, I am grateful for...

1 _____

2 _____

3 _____

Review your goals

Today's top 5 actions towards your goals.

☐ _____
☐ _____
☐ _____
☐ _____
☐ _____

I AM Affirmation

I AM

_____

Daily Reflection/Lessons Learned/Notes

_____

_____

My energy level

Tomorrow, I will...

1 _____

2 _____

3 _____

Day 84

My morning

☹ ☹ 😐 🙂 😊

Centering

☐ 3 Deep Breaths   ☐ Smiling Heart   ☐ Shine

Today's inspiration

Go confidently in the direction of your dreams. Live the life you have imagined.

Henry David Thoreau

Today, I am grateful for...

1 _____

_____

2 _____

_____

3 _____

_____

Review your goals

Today's top 5 actions towards your goals.

☐ _____

☐ _____

☐ _____

☐ _____

☐ _____

I AM Affirmation

I AM

_____

Daily Reflection/Lessons Learned/Notes

_____

_____

_____

My energy level

🔋🔋🔋🔋🔋

Tomorrow, I will...

1 _____

2 _____

3 _____

Woo hoo, way to go!

We hope that we were able to help you achieve your goals with this goal planner. You are the one who made it all happen. Great Job!

Now that you have made it through 12 weeks of daily journaling and goal planning, we have one more challenge for you.

For the next few days, follow the prompts and summarize the goals you have accomplished and lessons learned.

All by ourselves, with a pen and paper, WE GROW.

Day 85

Today's Date: _____ / _____ / 20_____

My morning
☹ ☹ 😐 🙂 😊

Centering

☐ 3 Deep Breaths   ☐ Smiling Heart   ☐ Shine

List all the goals you have achieved....

_____

_____

_____

_____

_____

_____

_____

_____

_____

My energy level

One amazing thing that happened today...

_____

_____

Day 86

Today's Date: _____/_____/ 20_____

My morning

☹ ☹ 😐 🙂 😊

Centering

☐ 3 Deep Breaths   ☐ Smiling Heart   ☐ Shine

What is your reward for each goal you've achieved?

_____

_____

_____

_____

_____

_____

_____

_____

My energy level

One amazing thing that happened today...

_____

_____

Day 87

My morning

☹ ☹ 😐 🙂 😃

Centering

☐ 3 Deep Breaths   ☐ Smiling Heart   ☐ Shine

Write down 3 things you have learned over the last 12 weeks

1 _____

_____

_____

2 _____

_____

_____

3 _____

_____

_____

My energy level

🔋🔋🔋🔋🔋

One amazing thing that happened today...

_____

_____

Day 88

Today's Date: _____/_____/ 20_____

My morning

☹ ☹ 😐 🙂 😃

Centering

☐ 3 Deep Breaths   ☐ Smiling Heart   ☐ Shine

3 things you can do to help 10 people in your community.

1 ....

....

....

2 ....

....

....

3 ....

....

....

My energy level

One amazing thing that happened today...

....

....

Day 89

My morning

☹ 😕 😐 🙂 😃

Centering

☐ 3 Deep Breaths   ☐ Smiling Heart   ☐ Shine

3 things you can do to help 1 million people in the world.

1 _____

_____

_____

2 _____

_____

_____

3 _____

_____

_____

My energy level

One amazing thing that happened today...

_____

_____

Day 90

My morning

☹ 🙁 😐 🙂 😀

Centering

☐ 3 Deep Breaths   ☐ Smiling Heart   ☐ Shine

3 GOALS you'd like to achieve over the NEXT 90 days

1 ....

....

....

....

2 ....

....

....

....

3 ....

....

....

....

My energy level

🔋🔋🔋🔋🔋

One amazing thing that happened today...

....

....

....

Congratulations!

YOU DID IT. Now, take a deep breath, smile and take a moment to enjoy this big accomplishment.

Remember that the path to becoming a leader is to take massive, determined actions. So make sure you take what you have learned and apply it to living your everyday life.

Ready to start your next "I AM A LEADER" journey?

We appreciate you picked up the "**I AM A LEADER**" goal planner and chose to embark on this exciting journey.

We know your journey of leadership won't stop here. Now, keep the momentum going and get your next "I AM A LEADER" goal planner at www.leadership4kids.com.

Thank you so much for your purchase!

If you find this journal helpful, please leave a review on Leadership4Kids.com to share you experience with others. We absolutely appreciate you!

Acknowledgment

I would like to acknowledge my teacher Douglas Lee, the founder of the Path to the Heart Foundation and his pioneering "Heart Method" for applying meditation, mindfulness and self-awareness to leadership development. You can learn more about the "Heart Method" from his website at https://www.ptthfoundation.com/

I would also like to acknowledge my family for their love and support. My wife Judy and my children, Benjamin (11 years-old) and Audrey (8 years-old) helped me with proofreading, examples, and suggestions during the editing process.

This journal drew inspirations from widely diverse sources, but the most important source of inspiration was the students who participated in my "Leadership4Kids" programs over the years. They taught me more than I taught them.

Peter J. Liang
Founder

LEADERSHIP4KIDS